"THE COMPASSIONATE 7: DEFENDERS OF THE MAGICAL FOREST" WAS BORN FROM A BURNING PASSION AND A HEARTFELT CAUSE. AS PARENTS AND EDUCATORS, WE DEEPLY UNDERSTAND THE IMPORTANCE OF FOSTERING A SENSE OF EMPATHY, UNDERSTANDING, AND EMOTIONAL INTELLIGENCE IN OUR CHILDREN. WE BELIEVE THAT THE SEEDS OF A KINDER, MORE INCLUSIVE WORLD CAN BE SOWN FROM AN EARLY AGE, ESPECIALLY WHEN IT COMES TO UNDERSTANDING AND APPRECIATING THOSE AMONG US WHO LIVE WITH DISABILITIES.

WEAVING TOGETHER THE THREADS OF IMAGINATION, COMPASSION, AND MODERN AI TOOLS, WE'VE CRAFTED A WORLD WHERE SEVEN UNIQUE SUPERHEROES, EACH WITH THEIR OWN DIFFERENCES AND ABILITIES, GUIDE LOST ANIMALS BACK HOME. THROUGH THEIR ADVENTURES, THEY DEMONSTRATE THAT OUR CHALLENGES CAN OFTEN BE OUR GREATEST STRENGTHS, SHOWING THAT WE ALL CAN BE HEROES IN OUR OWN SPECIAL WAYS.

BUT THE JOURNEY DOESN'T END THERE. IN ADDITION TO THE HEARTWARMING TALE, THE BOOK ALSO INCLUDES A SERIES OF INTERACTIVE DISABILITY AWARENESS GAMES. THESE FUN AND ENGAGING ACTIVITIES ARE DESIGNED TO PROVIDE AN INSIGHTFUL PERSPECTIVE INTO THE DAILY EXPERIENCES OF INDIVIDUALS WITH DIFFERENT DISABILITIES. THEY ENCOURAGE CHILDREN TO WALK IN OTHERS' SHOES, FOSTERING EMPATHY, AND PROMOTING INCLUSIVITY.

WE ARE MORE THAN JUST STORYTELLERS. WE ARE ADVOCATES, AIMING TO MAKE A DIFFERENCE IN THE WORLD. THEREFORE, PART OF THE PROFITS GENERATED FROM THIS BOOK WILL BE DONATED TO CAUSES AND ORGANIZATIONS THAT SUPPORT INDIVIDUALS WITH DISABILITIES.

SO, DEAR READER, PREPARE TO EMBARK ON A HEARTWARMING ADVENTURE OF COMPASSION, UNDERSTANDING, AND DISCOVERY. REMEMBER, EVERY PAGE YOU TURN NOT ONLY IGNITES IMAGINATION BUT ALSO CONTRIBUTES TO A CAUSE THAT CAN CHANGE LIVES.

THIS BOOK IS DEDICATED TO OUR LITTLE SUPERHERO - ALEXANDER

VISUAL IMPAIRMENT

HI THERE! DO YOU KNOW HOW SOMETIMES WHEN YOU'RE TRYING TO SEE SOMETHING FAR AWAY, LIKE A TINY BUG, IT'S REALLY HARD TO SEE? WELL, SOME PEOPLE HAVE A HARDER TIME SEEING THINGS THAN OTHERS. THIS IS CALLED VISUAL IMPAIRMENT, AND IT MEANS THAT THEIR EYES CAN'T SEE THINGS VERY WELL.

BUT DON'T WORRY, THERE ARE THINGS THAT CAN HELP! SOME PEOPLE NEED SPECIAL GLASSES TO HELP THEM SEE BETTER, AND OTHERS MIGHT USE A CANE TO HELP THEM WALK AROUND WITHOUT BUMPING INTO THINGS. IT'S LIKE HAVING A SUPERPOWER TO SEE IN THE DARK!

AND DID YOU KNOW THAT THERE IS A SPECIAL WAY THAT PEOPLE WHO CAN'T SEE CAN READ AND WRITE? IT'S CALLED BRAILLE! IT'S A SYSTEM OF RAISED DOTS THAT YOU CAN FEEL WITH YOUR FINGERS, LIKE A SECRET CODE. PEOPLE WHO KNOW BRAILLE CAN READ AND WRITE BOOKS AND STORIES, JUST LIKE YOU DO WITH YOUR EYES. IT'S REALLY AMAZING!

LUNA

MEET THE OWL NAMED LUNA!

LUNA IS AN INCREDIBLE OWL WHO WAS BORN WITHOUT THE ABILITY TO SEE.

EVEN WITHOUT HER EYESIGHT, LUNA LIVES LIFE TO ITS FULLEST.

WHAT MAKES HER SO SPECIAL IS HER HEIGHTENED SENSES – LUNA CAN HEAR EVEN THE FAINTEST NOISES FROM A LONG DISTANCE, AND SHE'S GOT A KEEN SENSE OF SMELL THAT HELPS HER LOCATE FOOD AND EXPLORE UNFAMILIAR PLACES.

LUNA IS AMAZING AT FORMING MENTAL MAPS WITH HER SENSES – SHE CAN IDENTIFY SHAPES AND OBSTACLES FROM SMELLS OR SOUNDS. HER FRIENDS ARE ALWAYS ASTONISHED BY HOW WELL SHE NAVIGATES THROUGH THE FOREST AND OFTEN ASK FOR HER HELP.

HEARING IMPAIRMENT

OUR EARS ARE AMAZING BECAUSE THEY HELP US HEAR SOUNDS. YOU KNOW, LIKE WHEN YOU LISTEN TO YOUR FAVORITE MUSIC OR WHEN YOU HEAR A BIRD SINGING. BUT SOMETIMES, OUR EARS NEED A LITTLE HELP TO HEAR THINGS CLEARLY. IT'S LIKE WHEN YOU'RE TRYING TO LISTEN TO SOMEONE TALKING, BUT THERE'S A LOT OF NOISE AROUND, LIKE WHEN THERE'S A LOUD TRUCK PASSING BY.

SOME PEOPLE HAVE A HARDER TIME HEARING SOUNDS THAN OTHERS. THEY MIGHT NEED SPECIAL THINGS TO HELP THEM HEAR BETTER, LIKE SPECIAL HEADPHONES. THESE SPECIAL THINGS ARE CALLED HEARING AIDS OR COCHLEAR IMPLANTS. THEY HELP PEOPLE HEAR BETTER AND MAKE SURE THEY DON'T MISS OUT ON ANY SOUNDS. IT'S LIKE HAVING SUPERPOWERS THAT HELP YOU HEAR THINGS EVEN WHEN THEY'RE REALLY QUIET!

BUT DID YOU KNOW THAT SOME PEOPLE CAN'T HEAR ANY SOUNDS AT ALL? THAT'S CALLED BEING COMPLETELY DEAF. BUT DON'T WORRY, THEY CAN STILL COMMUNICATE WITH OTHERS USING SIGN LANGUAGE. SIGN LANGUAGE IS LIKE TALKING WITH YOUR HANDS AND IT'S REALLY COOL! PEOPLE USE THEIR HANDS, ARMS, AND FACIAL EXPRESSIONS TO TELL STORIES AND HAVE CONVERSATIONS.

ANOTHER WAY PEOPLE CAN UNDERSTAND WHAT SOMEONE IS SAYING IS BY LIP READING. IT'S LIKE READING SOMEONE'S LIPS INSTEAD OF READING A BOOK. BY WATCHING THE MOVEMENT OF SOMEONE'S LIPS AND FACE, PEOPLE WHO ARE DEAF CAN STILL UNDERSTAND WHAT OTHERS ARE SAYING.

MEET HENRY - THE SILENT HARE.
HE IS BORN WITH A HEARING IMPAIRMENT THAT MAKES IT HARD FOR HIM TO HEAR SOFT OR DISTANT SOUNDS. BUT THAT DOESN'T STOP HIM FROM BEING A HERO!
IN FACT, HIS HEARING IMPAIRMENT GIVES HIM TWO SUPERPOWERS - LIP-READING AND SIGN LANGUAGE.

HENRY CAN UNDERSTAND WHAT OTHERS ARE SAYING EVEN FROM A DISTANCE JUST BY WATCHING THEIR LIPS, AND HE CAN COMMUNICATE SECRETLY WITHOUT MAKING A SOUND USING SIGN LANGUAGE

HENRY'S POWERS HELP HIM ON MANY ADVENTURES AND SUPERHERO SECRET MISSIONS IN THE MAGICAL FOREST, WHERE HE WORKS WITH HIS FRIENDS TO STOP THE FOREST VILLAINS FROM CAUSING TROUBLE. HENRY'S UNIQUE ABILITIES MAKE HIM AN IMPORTANT MEMBER OF THE TEAM, AND HE SHOWS THAT HAVING A HEARING IMPAIRMENT CAN'T STOP YOU FROM BEING A HERO!

MOBILITY IMPAIRMENT

YOU KNOW HOW WE USE OUR LEGS TO WALK, RUN, AND JUMP? WELL, SOMETIMES PEOPLE'S LEGS DON'T WORK VERY WELL, AND IT'S HARDER FOR THEM TO MOVE AROUND. IT'S LIKE WHEN WE TRY TO RUN THROUGH DEEP SNOW, IT CAN BE REALLY HARD TO MOVE FAST.

BUT DON'T WORRY, BECAUSE SOME PEOPLE HAVE REALLY COOL RIDES TO HELP THEM GET AROUND! SOME PEOPLE NEED A WHEELCHAIR OR CRUTCHES TO HELP THEM MOVE, AND THEY CAN GO ON ALL SORTS OF ADVENTURES WITH THEM.

SO, JUST BECAUSE SOME PEOPLE'S BODIES MOVE A LITTLE DIFFERENTLY THAN OURS, IT DOESN'T MEAN THEY CAN'T HAVE FUN AND EXPLORE THE WORLD TOO!

KODY
THE AMAZING KODY IS A SUPERHERO WHO IS ALWAYS READY TO HELP FRIENDS IN NEED.
HE HAS MOBILITY IMPAIRMENT AND USES A SPECIAL WHEELCHAIR TO HELP HIM MOVE AROUND. BUT THAT DOESN'T STOP HIM FROM BEING A HERO! HE HAS SUPER STRENGTH IN HIS ARMS AND SHOULDERS, WHICH ALLOWS HIM TO LIFT HEAVY OBJECTS, RACE AND EVEN DANCE. .
HIS WHEELCHAIR IS A SPY WEAPON THAT HELPS HIM SURVIVE IN DANGEROUS SITUATIONS.
KANGAROO-KICK INSPIRES HIS FRIENDS TO BELIEVE IN THEMSELVES AND NEVER GIVE UP, NO MATTER WHAT CHALLENGES THEY MAY FACE. HE SHOWS US THAT HAVING MOBILITY IMPAIRMENT DOESN'T MEAN YOU CAN'T BE A SUPERHERO AND MAKE A DIFFERENCE IN THE WORLD.

COGNITIVE IMPAIRMENT

OUR BRAIN IS LIKE A SUPER COMPUTER THAT HELPS US LEARN AND DO AMAZING THINGS, LIKE COUNTING AND READING A BOOK. BUT SOMETIMES OUR BRAIN WORKS A LITTLE DIFFERENTLY AND WE MIGHT NEED SOME EXTRA HELP TO LEARN NEW THINGS. IT'S LIKE WHEN WE'RE PUTTING TOGETHER A REALLY TOUGH PUZZLE, IT MIGHT TAKE A LITTLE LONGER TO FIGURE IT OUT. SOME PEOPLE NEED EXTRA TIME TO LEARN NEW THINGS, AND THAT'S OKAY. THEY MIGHT NEED A LITTLE EXTRA HELP OR SOME SPECIAL TOOLS TO HELP THEM LEARN AND DO THINGS. BUT JUST BECAUSE THEY LEARN DIFFERENTLY, IT DOESN'T MEAN THEY AREN'T SMART OR CAPABLE OF DOING AMAZING THINGS. IN FACT, THEY HAVE A SECRET POWER THAT ALLOWS THEM TO SEE THINGS IN A DIFFERENT WAY AND COME UP WITH UNIQUE IDEAS!

ANDY

INTRODUCING ANDY - THE INVENTIVE ANT!

HE MAY HAVE A COGNITIVE OR INTELLECTUAL IMPAIRMENT, WHICH MEANS HE SOMETIMES FINDS IT DIFFICULT TO UNDERSTAND OR LEARN NEW THINGS. BUT, WHAT SETS HIM APART IS HIS EXTRAORDINARY POWER OF CREATIVE IDEAS AND INNOVATIVE PROBLEM-SOLVING SKILLS.

WHENEVER ANDY FACES A CHALLENGE, HE SEES THINGS IN A NEW LIGHT AND COMES UP WITH INCREDIBLE SOLUTIONS THAT NO ONE ELSE COULD HAVE IMAGINED. HIS UNIQUE PERSPECTIVE AND RESOURCEFULNESS MAKE HIM AN INVALUABLE MEMBER OF ANY TEAM, AND HE INSPIRES OTHERS TO USE THEIR STRENGTHS TO HELP OTHERS TOO. DESPITE THE DIFFICULTIES HE FACES,

INVENTIVE ANT NEVER GIVES UP AND IS ALWAYS WILLING TO PUT IN THE EXTRA EFFORT TO ACHIEVE HIS GOALS. HIS SUPERPOWER SHOWS THAT EVERYONE HAS THEIR OWN UNIQUE STRENGTHS AND ABILITIES, AND THAT WE CAN ALL MAKE A DIFFERENCE IN THE WORLD BY USING THEM.

SPEECH IMPAIRMENT

OUR MOUTH HELPS US TALK AND SAY WORDS, BUT SOMETIMES WE MIGHT HAVE TROUBLE SAYING SOME WORDS. IT'S LIKE WHEN WE TRY TO SAY A REALLY LONG OR TRICKY WORD, IT MIGHT BE HARDER TO SAY. SOME PEOPLE MIGHT HAVE A HARDER TIME SPEAKING THAN OTHERS. THEY MIGHT NEED EXTRA HELP LEARNING HOW TO SAY CERTAIN WORDS OR MIGHT NEED MORE TIME TO PRACTICE.

SOMETIMES THEY MIGHT REPEAT SOME WORDS OR SOUNDS WHEN THEY TALK. BUT IT'S OKAY, EVERYONE HAS THEIR OWN WAY OF TALKING AND COMMUNICATING. IT'S LIKE HAVING A UNIQUE VOICE!

MEET TOMMY, THE TALKATIVE TOUCAN. HE IS A SUPERHERO WHO HAS A SPEECH IMPAIRMENT, BUT HE HAS DEVELOPED A UNIQUE WAY OF COMMUNICATION. HE CAN MIMIC DIFFERENT SOUNDS, WHICH ALLOWS HIM TO SPEAK WITH SECRET CODES AND MISLEAD HIS ENEMIES.

TOMMY USES HIS BEAK NOT JUST FOR EATING BUT ALSO AS A CODE DEVICE. HE USES HIS POWER OF MIMICRY TO HELP HIS FRIENDS AND DEFEAT VILLAINS. HE CAN IMITATE THE SOUNDS OF ANIMALS OR EVEN MACHINES, AND THIS MAKES HIM A VALUABLE MEMBER OF THE SUPERHERO TEAM.

TOMMY REMINDS US THAT EVEN THOUGH WE ARE DIFFERENT, WE CAN FIND WAYS TO COMMUNICATE AND USE OUR STRENGTHS TO HELP OTHERS.

MENTAL HEALTH IMPAIRMENT
OUR FEELINGS AND EMOTIONS HELP US UNDERSTAND HOW WE'RE
FEELING INSIDE. BUT SOMETIMES WE MIGHT FEEL SAD OR WORRIED
MORE OFTEN THAN WE WANT TO. IT'S LIKE WHEN WE'RE REALLY
EXCITED TO GO TO A BIRTHDAY PARTY, BUT THEN IT GETS
CANCELLED, WE MIGHT FEEL SAD. SOMETIMES PEOPLE'S FEELINGS AND
EMOTIONS CAN BE REALLY STRONG AND IT CAN BE HARD FOR THEM
TO FEEL HAPPY OR CALM. BUT THERE ARE THINGS WE CAN DO TO
HELP OURSELVES FEEL BETTER, LIKE TAKING DEEP BREATHS,
PRACTICING MEDITATION, OR TALKING TO A TRUSTED FRIEND OR
FAMILY MEMBER. WITH THE HELP OF THESE TOOLS, WE CAN LEARN TO
MANAGE OUR EMOTIONS AND FEEL BETTER. IT'S LIKE HAVING SUPER
EMOTIONAL POWERS THAT WE CAN LEARN TO CONTROL!

MAX
MEET MAX - THE MINDFUL MONKEY, A SUPERHERO WHO HAS A VERY SPECIAL POWER - THE POWER OF MEDITATION! MINDFUL MONKEY IS A MONKEY WHO HAS A MENTAL HEALTH IMPAIRMENT, WHICH MEANS THAT SOMETIMES HIS FEELINGS AND EMOTIONS CAN BE VERY STRONG AND OVERWHELMING. BUT HE HAS LEARNED HOW TO USE MEDITATION TO HELP CALM HIS MIND AND STAY FOCUSED.
MINDFUL MONKEY LOVES TO SHARE HIS SPECIAL POWER WITH OTHERS, AND HE USES IT TO HELP THOSE WHO ARE FEELING ANXIOUS, STRESSED, OR WORRIED. HE CAN HELP YOU TAKE DEEP BREATHS AND QUIET YOUR MIND, SO THAT YOU CAN FEEL MORE RELAXED AND CENTERED.
WHEN MINDFUL MONKEY IS NOT USING HIS POWERS TO HELP OTHERS, HE LOVES TO SPEND TIME IN NATURE AND CLIMB TREES. HE KNOWS THAT BEING IN NATURE IS A GREAT WAY TO CALM YOUR MIND AND FEEL MORE PEACEFUL.
MINDFUL MONKEY ALSO REMINDS US THAT IT'S IMPORTANT TO TAKE CARE OF OUR MENTAL HEALTH, JUST LIKE WE TAKE CARE OF OUR BODIES. HE ENCOURAGES EVERYONE TO TALK ABOUT THEIR FEELINGS, SEEK HELP WHEN NEEDED, AND PRACTICE MINDFULNESS TO STAY CENTERED AND BALANCED.
SO THE NEXT TIME YOU'RE FEELING ANXIOUS OR STRESSED, REMEMBER TO TAKE A DEEP BREATH AND THINK OF MINDFUL MONKEY. HE IS ALWAYS THERE TO HELP YOU FIND YOUR INNER CALM AND BE YOUR BEST SELF!

DOWN SYNDROME

DOWN SYNDROME IS A CONDITION THAT SOME PEOPLE ARE BORN WITH THAT CAN MAKE THEM LEARN AND GROW A LITTLE BIT DIFFERENTLY THAN OTHER PEOPLE.

IT HAPPENS WHEN SOMEONE HAS AN EXTRA SPECIAL THING CALLED A CHROMOSOME IN THEIR BODY. IT'S KIND OF LIKE HAVING AN EXTRA PUZZLE PIECE THAT MAKES THINGS LOOK A LITTLE BIT DIFFERENT. JUST LIKE HOW EVERYONE IS DIFFERENT IN THEIR OWN WAY, PEOPLE WITH DOWN SYNDROME ARE DIFFERENT TOO.

PEOPLE WITH DOWN SYNDROME ARE SPECIAL BECAUSE THEY HAVE SOME UNIQUE FEATURES THAT MAKE THEM STAND OUT. ONE OF THE THINGS THAT MAKES THEM SPECIAL IS THAT THEY HAVE A BEAUTIFUL SMILE THAT CAN LIGHT UP A ROOM.

LULU

SAY HELLO TO LULU, THE SUPERHERO WHO ALWAYS WEARS A SMILE!

LULU IS A VERY SPECIAL PANDA WHO HAS A VERY SPECIAL POWER - SHE CAN SPREAD HAPPINESS AND JOY WHEREVER SHE GOES!

EVEN THOUGH LULU MAY NOT BE THE FASTEST OR STRONGEST PANDA, SHE IS STILL A HERO BECAUSE OF HER KINDNESS AND CARING NATURE.

HER SUPERPOWER IS HER ABILITY TO MAKE PEOPLE FEEL GOOD ABOUT THEMSELVES AND THE WORLD AROUND THEM, JUST BY BEING HER HAPPY SELF. WHENEVER SOMEONE IS FEELING BLUE OR IN NEED OF A FRIEND, LULU IS ALWAYS THERE TO GIVE THEM A WARM HUG AND MAKE THEM FEEL BETTER.

7

THE SEVEN SUPERHEROES EACH POSSESSED THEIR OWN UNIQUE POWERS AND ABILITIES, BUT DESPITE THEIR DIFFERENCES, THEY ALL SHARED A COMMON GOAL:
TO USE THEIR POWERS FOR THE GREATER GOOD AND HELP THOSE IN NEED.

LOST IN THE MAGICAL FOREST
ONE DAY, A GROUP OF ANIMALS IN THE FOREST WAS IN TROUBLE. THEY WERE LOST AND COULDN'T FIND THEIR WAY BACK HOME. THEY WERE SCARED AND DIDN'T KNOW WHAT TO DO. THAT'S WHEN THE SEVEN SUPERHEROES CAME TO THEIR RESCUE.

ANDY USED HER INCREDIBLE CREATIVITY TO COME UP WITH A PLAN WHAT EACH OF THE SUPERHEROES HAD TO DO IN ORDER TO SUCCEED AND LEAD THE LOST ANIMALS BACK TO THEIR HOMES. SHE ALSO HELPED THEM FIND FOOD AND WATER ALONG THE WAY, USING HER PROBLEM-SOLVING SKILLS.

HENRY LEVERAGED HIS EXTRAORDINARY LIP-READING SKILLS TO UNDERSTAND WHAT EACH OF THE LOST AND SCARED ANIMALS WAS TRYING TO SAY AND UNDERSTAND WHERE THEY LIVE BECAUSE THEY ALL WERE TALKING OVER EACH OTHER. HE ALSO USED HIS SIGN-LANGUAGE SKILLS TO NAVIGATE THEM TOWARDS THEIR HOMES.

MAX APPROACHED THE ANIMALS AND ASKED THEM TO TAKE A DEEP BREATH AND CLOSE THEIR EYES. HE LED THEM THROUGH A CALMING MEDITATION THAT HELPED THEM FEEL MORE CENTERED AND LESS ANXIOUS. THEY WERE ABLE TO THINK MORE CLEARLY AND LISTEN TO WHAT THE 7 SUPERHEROES HAD TO SAY IN ORDER FOR THEM TO REACH THEIR HOMES SAFELY.

LULU HAD A UNIQUE ABILITY TO SENSE WHEN SOMEONE NEEDED A HUG. AFTER MAX LED THE ANIMALS THROUGH THE CALMING MEDITATION, LULU WENT AROUND HUGGING EACH OF THEM GENTLY, MAKING THEM FEEL SAFE AND LOVED. HER WARM AND COMFORTING EMBRACE HELPED TO CALM THEIR NERVES, AND THEY BEGAN TO FEEL MORE RELAXED AND LESS SCARED. LULU'S LOVING HUGS HAD MADE THEM FEEL BRAVE AND STRONG, AND THEY WERE READY TO FACE ANY CHALLENGES THAT LAY AHEAD.

SHE WAS SPREADING COMFORT AND LOVE WHEREVER SHE WENT WITH HER AMAZING SMILE. THE ANIMALS FELT GRATEFUL FOR LULU'S PRESENCE, AND THEY KNEW THAT WITH HER BY THEIR SIDE, THEY WOULD ALWAYS FEEL SAFE AND PROTECTED.

LUNA USED HER EXCEPTIONAL SENSE OF HEARING AND SMELL TO CREATE A MENTAL MAP OF THE FOREST. SHE WAS ABLE TO GUIDE THE ANIMALS THROUGH THE FOREST, AVOIDING ANY OBSTACLES AND MAKING SURE THEY STAYED SAFE.

TOMMY USED HIS BEAK TO CREATE DISTRACTING SOUNDS, WHICH SCARED OFF ANY PREDATORS THAT MIGHT HAVE BEEN LURKING NEARBY.

KODY USED HIS SPECIAL WHEELCHAIR TO CLEAR ANY OBSTACLES IN THEIR WAY AND MAKE SURE THE LOST ANIMALS ARRIVED HOME SAFELY. HE ALSO USED HIS SUPER STRENGTH TO CARRY SOME OF THE ANIMALS WHENEVER THEY WERE TOO TIRED TO WALK.

THANKS TO THE SEVEN SUPERHEROES' UNIQUE POWERS, THE ANIMALS WERE ABLE TO FIND THEIR WAY BACK HOME SAFELY. THEY THANKED THE SUPERHEROES FOR THEIR KINDNESS AND FOR USING THEIR POWERS TO HELP THOSE IN NEED.
BUT THE HEROES DID MORE THAN JUST SAVE THE DAY - THEY TAUGHT THE ANIMALS AN IMPORTANT LESSON. EACH AND EVERY ONE OF US HAS OUR OWN SPECIAL STRENGTHS AND ABILITIES THAT WE CAN USE TO HELP OTHERS. EVEN IF WE HAVE CHALLENGES OR DIFFERENCES, WE CAN STILL WORK TOGETHER AND COMMUNICATE EFFECTIVELY TO ACHIEVE OUR GOALS.

The End

DISCOVERING ABILITIES: FUN AND INTERACTIVE DISABILITY AWARENESS GAMES FOR CHILDREN AND PARENTS

THIS PART OF THE BOOK CONTAINS INTERACTIVE GAMES AND ACTIVITIES DESIGNED TO HELP CHILDREN AND PARENTS UNDERSTAND AND APPRECIATE VARIOUS DISABILITIES. EACH GAME IS SIMPLE AND ENGAGING, PROVIDING INSIGHT INTO THE DAILY CHALLENGES FACED BY INDIVIDUALS WITH DIFFERENT DISABILITIES. BY PARTICIPATING IN THESE GAMES, CHILDREN WILL DEVELOP EMPATHY AND BECOME MORE INCLUSIVE.

THROUGH THESE INTERACTIVE GAMES, CHILDREN AND PARENTS CAN BETTER UNDERSTAND AND APPRECIATE THE EXPERIENCES OF INDIVIDUALS WITH DISABILITIES. BY FOSTERING EMPATHY AND INCLUSIVITY, THESE ACTIVITIES CAN CREATE A MORE COMPASSIONATE AND UNDERSTANDING COMMUNITY.

YOU HEAR ME NOW?

OBJECTIVE: TO SIMULATE THE EXPERIENCE OF HEARING IMPAIRMENT AND PROMOTE UNDERSTANDING OF THE CHALLENGES PEOPLE WITH HEARING IMPAIRMENT FACE.

INSTRUCTIONS:

- HAVE THE CHILD WEAR HEADPHONES OR EARPLUGS TO SIMULATE HEARING IMPAIRMENT.
- THE PARENT SHOULD STAND A SHORT DISTANCE AWAY FROM THE CHILD AND SAY A SENTENCE OR PHRASE, SUCH AS "IT'S A BEAUTIFUL DAY OUTSIDE."
- THE CHILD SHOULD TRY TO REPEAT THE SENTENCE BACK TO THE PARENT AS ACCURATELY AS POSSIBLE.
- IF THE CHILD HAS DIFFICULTY UNDERSTANDING OR REPEATING THE SENTENCE, THE PARENT CAN REPEAT IT MORE SLOWLY OR CLEARLY.
- TAKE TURNS BEING THE LISTENER AND THE SPEAKER.
- AFTER THE GAME, DISCUSS THE EXPERIENCE AND HOW IT FELT TO HAVE DIFFICULTY UNDERSTANDING WHAT THE SPEAKER WAS SAYING. TALK ABOUT HOW PEOPLE WITH HEARING IMPAIRMENT MIGHT FEEL IN SIMILAR SITUATIONS, AND HOW WE CAN BE MORE UNDERSTANDING AND SUPPORTIVE OF THEM.

LIP READING CHALLENGE

OBJECTIVE: TO PRACTICE LIP READING AND DEVELOP COMMUNICATION SKILLS.

INSTRUCTIONS:

- ONE PERSON SAYS A PHRASE OR SENTENCE WITHOUT MAKING ANY SOUND, SUCH AS MOUTHING "HOW ARE YOU TODAY?"
- THE OTHER PERSON TRIES TO GUESS WHAT WAS SAID BASED ON LIP MOVEMENTS ALONE.
- IF THE GUESS IS INCORRECT, THE SPEAKER CAN REPEAT THE PHRASE OR SENTENCE.
- TAKE TURNS BEING THE SPEAKER AND THE GUESSER.
- AFTER THE GAME, DISCUSS THE EXPERIENCE AND HOW CHALLENGING IT CAN BE TO RELY SOLELY ON LIP READING FOR COMMUNICATION. TALK ABOUT HOW PEOPLE WITH HEARING IMPAIRMENT MIGHT USE LIP READING TO UNDERSTAND WHAT OTHERS ARE SAYING, AND HOW WE CAN BE MORE CONSIDERATE AND CLEAR IN OUR COMMUNICATION.

SIGN LANGUAGE CHARADES

OBJECTIVE: TO INTRODUCE BASIC SIGN LANGUAGE AND HIGHLIGHT ITS IMPORTANCE FOR INDIVIDUALS WITH HEARING IMPAIRMENTS.

INSTRUCTIONS:

- TEACH CHILDREN AND PARENTS SOME SIMPLE SIGN LANGUAGE GESTURES, SUCH AS GREETINGS, EMOTIONS, AND COMMON OBJECTS.
- AFTER PRACTICING, TAKE TURNS ACTING OUT THE SIGNS IN A GAME OF CHARADES.
- THE ACTOR CAN ONLY USE SIGN LANGUAGE TO CONVEY THE MESSAGE TO THE GUESSERS.
- IF THE GUESS IS INCORRECT, THE ACTOR CAN REPEAT THE SIGN OR OFFER A CLUE.
- TAKE TURNS BEING THE ACTOR AND THE GUESSER.
- AFTER THE GAME, DISCUSS THE IMPORTANCE OF SIGN LANGUAGE AS A COMMUNICATION TOOL FOR PEOPLE WITH HEARING IMPAIRMENTS. TALK ABOUT HOW IT CAN ENHANCE COMMUNICATION AND FOSTER INCLUSION AND UNDERSTANDING.

THE WHEELCHAIR OBSTACLE COURSE

OBJECTIVE: TO UNDERSTAND THE DAILY CHALLENGES FACED BY WHEELCHAIR USERS.
INSTRUCTIONS:

- SET UP A SIMPLE OBSTACLE COURSE USING EVERYDAY OBJECTS LIKE CHAIRS, TABLES, AND TOYS.
- HAVE CHILDREN AND PARENTS TAKE TURNS NAVIGATING THE COURSE WHILE SEATED IN A WHEELCHAIR OR A CHAIR WITH WHEELS.
- OBSERVE AND DISCUSS THE CHALLENGES FACED DURING THE ACTIVITY, SUCH AS TIGHT SPACES, UNEVEN SURFACES, OR OBSTACLES IN THE WAY.
- TALK ABOUT HOW THESE CHALLENGES CAN IMPACT A PERSON'S DAILY LIFE AND THE IMPORTANCE OF ACCESSIBILITY IN PUBLIC SPACES.
- BRAINSTORM WAYS TO MAKE SPACES MORE ACCESSIBLE AND INCLUSIVE FOR EVERYONE, SUCH AS ADDING RAMPS OR WIDER DOORWAYS.
- ENCOURAGE EMPATHY AND UNDERSTANDING FOR THOSE WHO MAY FACE PHYSICAL CHALLENGES IN THEIR DAILY LIVES.

MEMORY LANE

OBJECTIVE: TO EMPATHIZE WITH THE CHALLENGES FACED BY INDIVIDUALS WITH COGNITIVE DISABILITIES.
INSTRUCTIONS:

- SHOW CHILDREN AND PARENTS A SERIES OF IMAGES FOR A SHORT PERIOD (E.G. 10-15 SECONDS).
- AFTERWARD, ASK THEM TO RECALL AS MANY DETAILS AS POSSIBLE FROM THE IMAGES.
- DISCUSS THE DIFFICULTIES FACED DURING THE ACTIVITY AND HOW IT RELATES TO THE EXPERIENCES OF THOSE WITH COGNITIVE DISABILITIES, SUCH AS MEMORY OR ATTENTION DIFFICULTIES.
- TALK ABOUT DIFFERENT STRATEGIES THAT CAN HELP WITH MEMORY AND ATTENTION DIFFICULTIES, SUCH AS USING LISTS OR VISUAL AIDS.
- ENCOURAGE EMPATHY AND UNDERSTANDING FOR THOSE WHO MAY STRUGGLE WITH COGNITIVE DISABILITIES, AND EMPHASIZE THE IMPORTANCE OF SUPPORT AND ACCOMMODATIONS IN HELPING THEM SUCCEED.
- BRAINSTORM WAYS TO CREATE A MORE INCLUSIVE ENVIRONMENT FOR INDIVIDUALS WITH COGNITIVE DISABILITIES.

EMOTION PICTIONARY

OBJECTIVE: TO UNDERSTAND THE CHALLENGES FACED BY INDIVIDUALS WITH SOCIAL-EMOTIONAL DISABILITIES.
INSTRUCTIONS:

- WRITE VARIOUS EMOTIONS (E.G., HAPPY, SAD, ANGRY, SCARED) ON SLIPS OF PAPER AND PLACE THEM IN A BOWL.
- CHILDREN AND PARENTS TAKE TURNS DRAWING AN EMOTION FROM THE BOWL AND ILLUSTRATING IT ON A PIECE OF PAPER WITHOUT USING WORDS.
- THE OTHER PLAYERS GUESS THE EMOTION.
- DISCUSS THE CHALLENGES FACED DURING THE ACTIVITY AND HOW INDIVIDUALS WITH SOCIAL-EMOTIONAL DISABILITIES MIGHT STRUGGLE TO RECOGNIZE OR EXPRESS EMOTIONS.
- TALK ABOUT DIFFERENT TYPES OF SOCIAL-EMOTIONAL DISABILITIES, SUCH AS AUTISM OR ADHD, AND HOW THEY CAN AFFECT EMOTIONAL REGULATION AND EXPRESSION.
- BRAINSTORM WAYS TO CREATE A MORE INCLUSIVE ENVIRONMENT FOR INDIVIDUALS WITH SOCIAL-EMOTIONAL DISABILITIES, SUCH AS PROVIDING SOCIAL STORIES OR VISUAL SUPPORTS TO HELP RECOGNIZE AND EXPRESS EMOTIONS.
- ENCOURAGE EMPATHY AND UNDERSTANDING TOWARDS THOSE WHO MAY STRUGGLE WITH SOCIAL-EMOTIONAL DISABILITIES, AND PROMOTE A CULTURE OF ACCEPTANCE AND SUPPORT.

EYE SPY WITH A TWIST

OBJECTIVE: TO UNDERSTAND THE CHALLENGES FACED BY INDIVIDUALS WITH VISUAL IMPAIRMENTS.
INSTRUCTIONS:

- BLINDFOLD ONE PLAYER AND PLAY A GAME OF "EYE SPY" WITH A TWIST.
- INSTEAD OF SIMPLY IDENTIFYING OBJECTS BY SIGHT, ENCOURAGE THE BLINDFOLDED PLAYER TO USE THEIR OTHER SENSES, SUCH AS TOUCH OR SMELL, TO IDENTIFY OBJECTS AROUND THEM.
- USE COMMON OBJECTS, SUCH AS A TOY OR A PIECE OF FRUIT, AND ASK THE BLINDFOLDED PLAYER TO IDENTIFY THEM WITHOUT USING THEIR SENSE OF SIGHT.
- DISCUSS THE CHALLENGES FACED DURING THE ACTIVITY AND HOW INDIVIDUALS WITH VISUAL IMPAIRMENTS MIGHT USE TOOLS LIKE BRAILLE OR GUIDE DOGS TO NAVIGATE THEIR SURROUNDINGS.
- EXPLORE DIFFERENT TYPES OF VISUAL IMPAIRMENTS, SUCH AS NEARSIGHTEDNESS OR COLOR BLINDNESS, AND HOW THEY AFFECT VISION.
- BRAINSTORM WAYS TO MAKE ENVIRONMENTS MORE ACCESSIBLE FOR INDIVIDUALS WITH VISUAL IMPAIRMENTS, SUCH AS USING HIGH-CONTRAST COLORS OR AUDIO CUES.
- ENCOURAGE EMPATHY AND UNDERSTANDING TOWARDS THOSE WHO MAY STRUGGLE WITH VISUAL IMPAIRMENTS, AND PROMOTE A CULTURE OF ACCESSIBILITY AND INCLUSION.

BLINDFOLDED DAILY ROUTINE CHALLENGE

OBJECTIVE: TO UNDERSTAND THE CHALLENGES FACED BY INDIVIDUALS WITH VISUAL IMPAIRMENTS IN COMPLETING DAILY TASKS.
INSTRUCTIONS: BLINDFOLD ONE PLAYER AND ASK THEM TO COMPLETE A SIMPLE DAILY TASK, SUCH AS GETTING DRESSED OR MAKING A SANDWICH, WHILE NAVIGATING THROUGH THE HOUSE. THE OTHER PLAYERS CAN OFFER VERBAL GUIDANCE AND SUPPORT. AFTERWARDS, DISCUSS THE CHALLENGES FACED DURING THE ACTIVITY AND HOW INDIVIDUALS WITH VISUAL IMPAIRMENTS USE TOOLS LIKE BRAILLE OR GUIDE DOGS TO NAVIGATE THEIR SURROUNDINGS. BRAINSTORM WAYS TO MAKE ENVIRONMENTS MORE ACCESSIBLE FOR INDIVIDUALS WITH VISUAL IMPAIRMENTS, SUCH AS USING HIGH-CONTRAST COLORS OR AUDIO CUES. ENCOURAGE EMPATHY AND UNDERSTANDING TOWARDS THOSE WHO MAY STRUGGLE WITH VISUAL IMPAIRMENTS, AND PROMOTE A CULTURE OF ACCESSIBILITY AND INCLUSION.

AFFIRMATION MIRROR

OBJECTIVE: TO DEVELOP POSITIVE SELF-TALK AND BUILD SELF-ESTEEM.

INSTRUCTIONS: HAVE CHILDREN AND PARENTS STAND IN FRONT OF A MIRROR AND TAKE TURNS SAYING POSITIVE AFFIRMATIONS TO THEMSELVES, SUCH AS "I AM BRAVE" OR "I AM SMART." ENCOURAGE THEM TO REPEAT THESE AFFIRMATIONS TO THEMSELVES THROUGHOUT THE DAY, ESPECIALLY DURING TIMES WHEN THEY MIGHT FEEL DOWN OR UNCERTAIN. DISCUSS THE IMPORTANCE OF POSITIVE SELF-TALK AND HOW IT CAN HELP BUILD SELF-ESTEEM AND CONFIDENCE.

SUPERHEROES WITH DISABILITIES: EXPLORING REAL-LIFE EXAMPLES
SIMILAR TO THE MAGICAL FOREST SUPERHEROES THAT YOU HAVE RECENTLY READ ABOUT, NUMEROUS HUMAN SUPERHEROES HAVE HAD DISABILITIES. YOU CAN EXPLORE AND DISCOVER THE NAMES OF THESE SUPERHEROES LISTED BELOW AND RESEARCH MORE ABOUT THEM TOGETHER:

	ONE OF THE MOST FAMOUS INVENTORS OF ALL TIME, AND HE WAS ALSO DEAF. DESPITE HIS HEARING IMPAIRMENT, HE INVENTED THE PHONOGRAPH, THE MOTION PICTURE CAMERA, AND THE ELECTRIC LIGHT BULB, AMONG OTHER THINGS.
	A FAMOUS ENTREPRENEUR AND FOUNDER OF THE VIRGIN GROUP. HE HAS DYSLEXIA, WHICH MADE IT DIFFICULT FOR HIM TO READ AND WRITE AS A CHILD. DESPITE THIS, HE HAS BECOME ONE OF THE MOST SUCCESSFUL BUSINESSMEN IN THE WORLD.
	A FAMOUS ARTIST WHO HAS AUTISM. HE HAS AN INCREDIBLE ABILITY TO DRAW DETAILED CITYSCAPES FROM MEMORY AFTER ONLY SEEING THEM ONCE.
	THE KING OF THE UNITED KINGDOM DURING WORLD WAR II, AND HE HAD A SEVERE STUTTER THAT MADE IT DIFFICULT FOR HIM TO SPEAK IN PUBLIC. DESPITE THIS, HE GAVE SEVERAL IMPORTANT SPEECHES THAT INSPIRED THE BRITISH PEOPLE DURING THE WAR.
	A FAMOUS SINGER AND ACTRESS WHO HAS BEEN OPEN ABOUT HER STRUGGLES WITH MENTAL HEALTH, INCLUDING DEPRESSION AND ANXIETY. DESPITE THESE CHALLENGES, SHE HAS CONTINUED TO PERFORM AND ADVOCATE FOR MENTAL HEALTH AWARENESS. FAMOUS SONG – BLOODY MARY
	THE AUTHOR OF THE HARRY POTTER SERIES, AND SHE HAS ALSO BEEN OPEN ABOUT HER STRUGGLES WITH MENTAL HEALTH, INCLUDING DEPRESSION. DESPITE THESE CHALLENGES, SHE HAS BECOME ONE OF THE MOST SUCCESSFUL AUTHORS IN THE WORLD.
	A DISABILITY RIGHTS ADVOCATE AND ACCOMPLISHED SWIMMER WHO HAS SWUM ACROSS THE ENGLISH CHANNEL AND COMPLETED MULTIPLE OTHER LONG-DISTANCE SWIMS. THE FIRST LIVING PERSON WITH DOWN SYNDROME TO RECEIVE AN HONORARY DOCTORATE DEGREE FROM THE UNIVERSITY OF PORTLAND IN 2013 .

	A FAMOUS MUSICIAN WHO WAS BORN BLIND. HE LEARNED TO PLAY SEVERAL MUSICAL INSTRUMENTS AND HAS WON 25 GRAMMY AWARDS THROUGHOUT HIS CAREER.
	A FAMOUS MEXICAN ARTIST WHO HAD POLIO AS A CHILD, WHICH CAUSED HER TO HAVE A LIMP. LATER, SHE WAS IN A TERRIBLE BUS ACCIDENT THAT LEFT HER WITH SEVERE INJURIES, INCLUDING A BROKEN SPINE. DESPITE HER INJURIES, KAHLO CONTINUED TO PAINT AND BECAME ONE OF THE MOST FAMOUS ARTISTS OF THE 20TH CENTURY.
	A FAMOUS PHYSICIST WHO WAS DIAGNOSED WITH A MOTOR NEURON DISEASE AT THE AGE OF 21. THE DISEASE GRADUALLY LEFT HIM PARALYZED, AND HE HAD TO COMMUNICATE THROUGH A SPEECH-GENERATING DEVICE. DESPITE HIS DISABILITY, HAWKING MADE GROUNDBREAKING DISCOVERIES IN PHYSICS AND BECAME ONE OF THE MOST FAMOUS SCIENTISTS IN THE WORLD.
	A FAMOUS COMPOSER WHO BECAME DEAF LATER IN LIFE. DESPITE HIS DEAFNESS, HE CONTINUED TO COMPOSE MUSIC AND CREATED SOME OF THE MOST FAMOUS PIECES IN CLASSICAL MUSIC HISTORY.
	THE 32ND PRESIDENT OF THE UNITED STATES AND HAD POLIO, WHICH LEFT HIM PARALYZED FROM THE WAIST DOWN. DESPITE HIS DISABILITY, HE LED THE COUNTRY THROUGH SOME OF ITS TOUGHEST TIMES, INCLUDING THE GREAT DEPRESSION AND WORLD WAR II.
	ONE OF THE MOST FAMOUS SCIENTISTS OF ALL TIME, AND HE IS BELIEVED TO HAVE HAD DYSLEXIA, WHICH MADE IT DIFFICULT FOR HIM TO READ AND WRITE AS A CHILD. DESPITE THIS, HE WENT ON TO DEVELOP THE THEORY OF RELATIVITY AND REVOLUTIONIZE THE FIELD OF PHYSICS.
	THE PRIME MINISTER OF THE UNITED KINGDOM DURING WORLD WAR II AND HAD A SPEECH IMPEDIMENT THAT MADE IT DIFFICULT FOR HIM TO SPEAK CLEARLY. DESPITE THIS, HE INSPIRED THE BRITISH PEOPLE AND HELPED LEAD THE COUNTRY TO VICTORY.
	A FAMOUS ITALIAN TENOR WHO IS BLIND. DESPITE HIS VISUAL IMPAIRMENT, HE HAS SOLD MILLIONS OF RECORDS AND HAS PERFORMED FOR AUDIENCES AROUND THE WORLD.

TITLE: THE COMPASSIONATE 7
SUBTITLE: DEFENDERS OF THE MAGICAL FOREST

CONTRIBUTORS: TEODOR EVSTRATIEV, AND ANNA TSEKOVA

ILLUSTRATIONS GENERATED VIA MIDJOURNEY AND EDITED BY MARTINA ANGELOVA

THIS BOOK WAS PRODUCED WITH THE ASSISTANCE OF OPENAI'S CHATGPT AND EDITED BY DEA DONCHEVA

PUBLISHED BY BRIGHTFUTUREBOOKS
LONDON, UNITED KINGDOM
WEBSITE: WWW.BRIGHTFUTUREBOOKS.COM

ISBN: 9786199252512
FIRST EDITION: 2023

Printed by printing house "FoliArt" Dobrich